Take Away Three

Tana Reiff

LifeTimes™ 2 Titles

Take Away Three
Climbing the Wall
The Door Is Open
Just for Today
Chicken by Che
Play Money
The Missing Piece

Cover illustration: Terry Hoff

Printed in the United States of America
6 7 8 9 10 04 03 02 01

ISBN 0–822–44602–2

Library of Congress Catalog Card Number: 87–80034

Contents

CHAPTER 1 1
CHAPTER 2 6
CHAPTER 3 9
CHAPTER 4 13
CHAPTER 5 18
CHAPTER 6 22
CHAPTER 7 26
CHAPTER 8 32
CHAPTER 9 35
CHAPTER 10 39
CHAPTER 11 43
CHAPTER 12 47
CHAPTER 13 50
CHAPTER 14 55

CHAPTER 1

"Carol, I'm home,"
Rennie called.
Rennie was a truck driver.
He had been on the road
for a week.

"I thought you were
coming home tomorrow,"
said Carol.
She had a strange look
on her face.

Rennie heard a noise.
It was the back door.

"Who just left?"
Rennie asked Carol.
"One of the kids?"

"No," said Carol.
"It was no one."

"Who was it?"
Rennie asked again.

"It was Gary,"
said Carol.
"Are you happy now?"

"Who's Gary?"
Rennie wanted to know.
"Is this some guy
you're seeing
while I'm on the road?"

Carol began to cry.
"You're never home, Rennie.
And when you are,
you're no fun.
You're always tired.
You shout at me.
You tell me
what to do.
And you never help
around the house.
I'm not happy.

So that's why
I see Gary."

Rennie was
really angry now.
"We have two kids
and you bring another man
into this house?
It's no good, Carol.
I'm leaving."

"Where are you going?"
Carol asked.

"The company wanted me
to go to the coast
for six days,"
said Rennie.
"I said no.
I needed a break.
But now I'm going to go.
Good-bye Carol.
I don't want to say
what I think of you
right now."

"But wait, Rennie,"
begged Carol.
"Don't you want
to talk about this?"

"No," said Rennie.
"What is there
to talk about?
I'll be back
in six days.
Have a good time
while I'm away."

He banged the door
on his way out.

Thinking It Over

1. What do you think
   of Carol's bringing Gary
   to the house?

2. If Carol is right
   about Rennie,
   what do you think
   of how he acts?

3. Do you think
   people should talk things over
   when a problem comes up?

CHAPTER 2

Six days later
Rennie was headed home.
He was very tired.
The trip had seemed long.
The traffic had been very heavy.
He was worried
about the fight with Carol.
But he hadn't
called her all week.

He decided
to stop and call her.
He tried,
but no one
answered the phone.

Rennie drove
another 50 miles.
He stopped again and tried
to call Carol again.
There was still no answer.

So Rennie kept on driving.
There were 30 miles left.
Then 20.
Then 10.
He dropped off the rig
and picked up his car.
He drove home.

When he got there
the place
was quiet.
There was no car
in front of the house.

Rennie went inside.
He stopped dead
in his tracks.
The house was empty.
Everything was gone.
Carol and the kids
were gone.
He felt
as empty as the house.

Carol hadn't even
left a note.

Thinking It Over

1. What do you do
   to keep awake on the road?

2. Should Rennie have called
   Carol before he did?

3. If you were Rennie,
   what would you do now?

CHAPTER 3

Rennie walked
through the house.
"Maybe the phone works,"
he thought to himself.
He tried the phone.
It was still working.

He called Carol's mother.
"Where's Carol?"
he asked.
"Where are Pete and Jill?
I just got home
and no one is here.
Nothing is here!"

"I can't talk about it,"
Carol's mother said.
She hung up.

Rennie called
Carol's friends.

They seemed to know
something was going on.
But they didn't know what.
"Sorry, Rennie,"
they all told him.
"We'll let you know
if we hear anything."

"I just know
she's with that Gary,"
Rennie thought.
"But I'm not about
to call him.
I don't even know
his last name.
And if Carol
is with Gary,
where are the kids?"

Rennie looked
around the house
for a clue.
Every room was empty.
But wait.
He found

his clothes
and his sleeping bag
in the closet.
And Carol had left
a toothbrush
in the bathroom.

He didn't know
who else to call.
He didn't know
where to look
for Carol and Pete and Jill.
He was very upset.
But he was also very tired.
So he brushed his teeth.
Then he rolled out
the sleeping bag.
He felt sad and lonely.
But finally he fell asleep.
Maybe tomorrow
he would find out
what was going on.

Thinking It Over

1. What do you think
   of what Carol did?

2. What do you do
   if you can't sleep?

3. Is there always hope
   for tomorrow?

CHAPTER 4

The mail came
at about 10:00
the next morning.
The sound of the mail
falling on the floor
woke Rennie up.

He looked around.
It wasn't a dream.
Carol and the kids
and everything were gone.

He got out of
the sleeping bag.
He wanted to see the mail.

There was a letter
from a lawyer.
He opened it.
He couldn't believe
what the letter said.

Carol was filing
for divorce.

Rennie had to talk to her.
He had to talk her
out of a divorce.
He called her
at her office.
Sure enough,
she was at work.

"I'm sorry,"
Rennie told her.
"I'm not a good husband.
I'm away too much.
I just don't know
how else to make a living."

"I know you
have to make a living
the best way you can,"
said Carol.

"Thanks,"
said Rennie.

"But I want you
and Pete and Jill.
I can't live
without you."

"Of course you can,"
said Carol.
"You live quite well
without us
all the time."

"That's not true,"
Rennie said.
"Sure, I like the road.
But I like
coming home to you, too.
Let's try
to work this out.
Let's see
a marriage counselor."

"Don't you remember?"
Carol said.
"We already did that once.
It didn't work.

Nothing changed.
You wouldn't change at all.
Besides, it's not just your job.
It's you.
You just don't care.
Forget it, Rennie.
We're living
with my mother.
The marriage is over."
She hung up the phone.

Rennie sat
on the floor
and cried.
"She means it
this time,"
he thought.
"What am I
going to do?"

Thinking It Over

1. Why do some marriages
   break up?

2. When a marriage breaks up,
   is it because of one person
   or both?

3. Do you believe people
   who promise to change
   but never keep their word?

CHAPTER 5

Rennie went
on his next road trip.
When he got back,
there was
another letter
from Carol's lawyer.
It said that
at least for now,
the children
would live with Carol
and their grandmother.
Rennie could see
Pete and Jill
when he was home.

That day
Rennie found
a smaller place to live.
He could move in
right away.

But he had
nothing to move.
Carol had taken
all the furniture.
She had taken
the dishes,
the pots and pans,
and everything.

Carol said
she would give back
some furniture.
After all,
some of it
had come
from Rennie's family.

Rennie didn't
just want the children
to visit him.
He wanted them
to stay overnight sometimes.
He promised Carol
that he would buy beds
for Pete and Jill.

"Maybe I didn't make
a good husband,"
he told Carol.
"But I still
have a crack
at being a good father."

"OK," Carol said.
"Maybe
you can still be
a good father."

Thinking It Over

1. Who should children live with—
their mother or father?

2. Suppose someone gave you
a present that came
from his or her family.
If you stopped being friends,
what would you do
with the present?

3. Can a man be a good father
if he's not a good husband?

CHAPTER 6

Rennie wanted
to be home more often.
He wanted to see
Pete and Jill
as much as possible.
So he asked
the trucking company
for short runs.
He would make
less money
this way.
But he would be
home most nights.

"Just one more thing,"
said Rennie
to his boss.
"May I borrow
a small truck
for the day?
I have to move.

But first,
I have to buy
some things to move!"

The boss
felt sorry for Rennie.
"Sure, take a small truck.
You must get used to driving one
for the short runs, right?"

Rennie drove the truck
to a used furniture store.
He had $300.
He bought
some old chairs.
He bought
two old tables.
He bought beds
for the kids.
He bought a bed
for himself.
He bought some lamps.
He bought some pots and pans.
He bought
bright orange dishes.

He even bought
an old black and white
TV set.

It was fun.
He couldn't believe
how much he bought
for $300.

Rennie packed the truck.
He drove the whole mess
to his new apartment.

Rennie stayed up late
that night.
He cleaned
everything he bought.
Then he placed
the furniture
all around the apartment.

"Not bad,"
he said to himself
as he looked around.
"I hope the kids
like the new place."

Thinking It Over

1. What's the best buy
   you ever got?

2. What stores in your area
   have the best buys?

3. Do you like
   to fix up your home?
   How does it make you feel?

CHAPTER 7

Pete and Jill
came to visit Rennie.
They had not
seen him
since they moved
to their grandmother's.

"How do you
like the new place?"
Rennie asked.

Pete looked around.
"It's all right,"
he said.

"It's OK,"
said Jill.
"But Gary's place
is nicer."

"Don't talk
about your mother's friends,"
Rennie told Jill.
He was angry.
"I don't want
to hear about Gary."

"Can we watch TV?"
Pete asked.

"You just got here,"
said Rennie.

Pete turned on
the TV anyway.
"Oh, no,"
he said.
"It's not color.
Even Grandma
has a color TV!"

"OK, then,"
said Rennie.
"Let's make
dinner together."

"Grandma doesn't
make us cook,"
said Jill.
"She doesn't make us
do anything!"

"OK, OK,"
said Rennie.
"Let's go out
to eat.
Then we can go
to a movie.
How does that sound?"

So the three of them
ate fast food.
They saw a movie
that Rennie wanted to see.

"How did you like
the movie?"
Rennie asked.

"No good,"
said Pete.

"I didn't
understand it."

They drove home
without talking.

"I'll show you
your new beds,"
said Rennie.

Pete and Jill
started jumping
on the beds.

"Don't do that,"
Rennie said.
"Now get ready for bed.
It's time to sleep."

The kids got into
their beds.

"I can't sleep,"
called Jill.
"The bed smells funny."

"I can't sleep either,"
called Pete.
"My bed smells funny, too."

"OK, that's it,"
Rennie shouted back.
"Get dressed.
You're going
back to Grandma's
right this minute.
You can sleep there.
Now move it."

Thinking It Over

1. How much should children help out around the house?

2. Why does nothing seem right to the children?

3. When parents break up, how much does it matter to their children?

CHAPTER 8

Carol called Rennie
the next day.
"Not such a good visit
with the kids, huh?"
she asked.

She told Rennie
the kids were both
having trouble
at school.
Their teachers
wanted to talk
to the parents.

"I'll go,"
said Rennie.
"I have some days off.
You have to work."

Carol was surprised.
Rennie had never gone
to the school before.

So Rennie talked
with both teachers.
"I'm sorry
that Pete and Jill
are both having trouble,"
he said.
"Divorce is hard
on children, too."

"Yes, it is,"
said Pete's teacher.
"Just take it slow.
Don't push them.
But don't let them
get away with things either.
Help them
with their schoolwork.
Be there
when they need you."

"You can count on it,"
said Rennie.
"I feel like
I'm climbing a mountain.
But things will get better."

Thinking It Over

1. In what ways
   is Rennie changing?

2. Think of three reasons
   why some children
   have trouble in school.

3. Can you think of a time
   when you felt as if
   you were climbing a mountain?

CHAPTER 9

Rennie was
home alone one night.
He heard a knock
on the door.
It was Mrs. Black,
his new neighbor.

"I have a present
for you,"
said Mrs. Black.
"It's a cookbook.
My husband did
all the cooking
at our house.
When he died,
I had to cook.
Think of it!
After all those years,
I had to learn to cook!
I couldn't have done it

without this cookbook.
Here, it's for you."

A long time ago
Rennie had worked
as a short-order cook.
When he got married,
Carol did
all the cooking.
She did
all the food shopping, too.

"You cooked before,"
said Mrs. Black.
"You can learn again.
Just remember one thing.
If you can read,
you can cook!"

Rennie laughed.
"If you can read,
you can cook!
I'll remember that."

"And remember this, too,"

said Mrs. Black.
“Remember to buy
everything you need
before you need it!”

“Thanks for the cookbook,”
said Rennie.
“And thanks
for stopping by.”

Thinking It Over

1. Why is Mrs. Black's present such a good one?

2. What small presents do you remember best?

3. What is a good neighbor?

CHAPTER 10

Pete and Jill
came to visit again.
Rennie hoped
things would go better
this time.
He had bought
lots of good food.
This time
he and the kids
would cook together.

But Jill and Pete
still didn't want to cook.
"Grandma and Mom
don't make us cook,"
the cried.

"Well, I'm not Mom,"
said Rennie.
"And I'm not Grandma.
And I'm not Gary, either.

I'm Dad.
And we're
going to cook together."

"Where did you
learn to cook, anyway?"
Pete wondered.
"I never saw you cook."

"It's like this,"
laughed Rennie.
"If you can read,
you can cook.
Now where's
my cookbook?"

So Rennie, Pete, and Jill
made a great dinner.
They made chicken.
They baked rolls.
They cut up vegetables
and made a salad.
They ate together
on the bright orange dishes.

Then they cleaned up
the mess.

After dinner,
Rennie helped
Pete and Jill
with their schoolwork.

Thinking It Over

1. Why could Rennie
   get the kids to cook
   this time?

2. Can you cook
   without having to read?

3. What's a good dinner
   to make with children?

CHAPTER 11

Rennie was doing
better and better
on his own.
However, he missed Carol.
He missed
living with her
and the kids.

One day
Carol called him.
"I found
a place to live,"
she told him.
"Can you
help me move?"

"Help you move?"
said Rennie.
"Why don't you
ask Gary to help?"

"Gary is
out of my life,"
said Carol.
"He said
it's not the same
since I left you.
He started going out
with another woman
at the office.
How do you like that?"

Rennie said nothing.
He couldn't
believe his ears.
"I'll help you move,"
he said.
"But only because
I want to help
the children."

"Thank you, Rennie,"
said Carol.
"Can you do it Saturday?"

"Yes, yes,"
Rennie answered.

"But, listen to me, Carol.
I'm making it
on my own.
It was your choice
to leave.
You should learn
to make it
on your own, too."

"I guess you're right,"
said Carol.
"But thanks
for helping us move."

"You think
all men
are bad news,
don't you?"
Rennie asked Carol.

"Not you,"
said Carol.
"You're changing.
And I like it."

Thinking It Over

1. What does a man like Gary
   seem to want in a woman?

2. Should Carol
   be asking Rennie
   to help her out?

CHAPTER 12

A few weeks later
Rennie's company
needed him
for a long trip.
It was
the first time
he had been
on a long ride
since Carol left.

The second night out
he met a pretty woman.
They went dancing.

"Let me
tell you something,"
Rennie told the woman.
"I was on the road
for ten years
while I was married.

I could have had
a good time
with lots of other women.
But I never did.
I was always true
to Carol."

"I don't believe you,"
laughed the woman.

"Well, it's true,"
said Rennie.
"Let's dance."

Rennie had not danced
with another woman
for 12 years.
It was nice
to be with a woman.
But this woman
was not Carol.
This woman was nice,
but she was different.
Rennie missed Carol
more than ever.

Thinking It Over

1. Do you think it's OK
   for Rennie to dance
   with another woman?

2. Why do you think
   Rennie told the woman
   he had been true to Carol?

3. Do you think
   people who work on the road
   can be happily married?

CHAPTER 13

Pete and Jill
were coming to visit
for the whole weekend.
Rennie was glad
to spend the time
with them.
He made plans
to go to the park.
They loved the rides.
Rennie did, too.

He was getting ready
to pick up the kids.
Then he heard a car
pull up out front.
He looked
out the window.
It was Carol,
dropping off the kids.
She had never done that.

Rennie watched
Carol get out
of the car.
She was
all dressed up.
She looked beautiful.
Rennie heard
the three of them
climbing the steps.
He heard Carol
ring the bell.

Rennie answered
the door.
"Hi," he said.
"I didn't think
I would see you, Carol."

Carol told
Pete and Jill
to go play.
She wanted
to talk to Rennie
by herself.

"Rennie," she said.
"I think maybe
I acted too fast.
I moved out
when I was
very angry.
I filed for divorce
right away.
Maybe it was
all too fast."

"Maybe it had to happen,"
said Rennie.
"You put up
with a lot
from me.
I had
some growing up
to do."

"Maybe," said Carol.

"You look great,"
Rennie said.

"Are you looking
so good
because Gary
isn't around?"

"No, Rennie,"
said Carol.
"I'm looking good
for you."

Thinking It Over

1. Do some people
   get divorced too fast?

2. Do you think divorce laws
   help people divorce too fast?

3. Is it possible for people
   to break up
   and fall in love again?

CHAPTER 14

The boss
called Rennie
into his office.

"Rennie," he said,
"The company has
a little problem.
We just don't need
short-run drivers
from this station
right now.
You have
two choices.
You can stay here
and do long runs.
Or you can move
to another city
and do short runs."

"I'll think about it,"
Rennie told the boss.

When he got home,
he called Carol.
He told her
about his two choices.

"What should I do?"
he asked her.
"I'd rather
be near the kids.
And I'd like
to be near
their mother, too."

"That would be nice,"
said Carol.
"But you must decide
what to do."

"If I stay,
my job will be
just like before,"
Rennie said.
"I won't be home
very much."

"It would be nice
to have you
in the same town,"
said Carol.

"OK," said Rennie.
"I'll stay and do
the long runs.
But let's not
rush into anything.
I mean
about you and me.
Let's just see
what happens."

"I'm glad
you'll be near,"
said Carol.

"Me, too,"
Rennie said.
"Maybe, just maybe
things will work out.
Maybe we can be

a family again.
Maybe we should see
a marriage counselor again.
Getting together
won't be easy.
But I'll try
if you will."

"I'll start
by calling off
the divorce,"
said Carol.
"What do you think?"

"You're on,"
said Rennie.
"Talk to you tomorrow."

Thinking It Over

1. Would you change your job
   to help someone else?

2. People say "marriage is
   a two-way street."
   What does that mean?

3. What will Rennie and Carol
   have to do
   to save their marriage?

4. Do you think Rennie's changes
   will make a difference
   if he and Carol
   get back together?